Grateful recognition is given to W. E. Harnish, Associate Professor of Education and Supervisor of Student Teaching in Science, Emeritus, University of Illinois, Urbana, Illinois, for his helpful suggestions.

Published simultaneously in the Dominion of Canada by George J. McLeod Limited, Toronto.

Printed in the United States of America.

Library of Congress Catalog Card No. 57-7182

SHADOW

Written and Illustrated by Larry Kettelk

WILLIAM MORROW & COMPANY

Contents

SHADOW FUN

A shadow is a strange thing. It is a place where there is no direct light, yet without light no shadow can exist at all. When a solid object blocks the passage of light it casts a shadow on another object or surface. This shadow gives us the outline of the object that created it. It is a simple silhouette and has no detail other than the edges of the original object.

5

There is something fascinating about your own shadow. When you walk in the bright sunshine in the middle of the day, it seems to be shriveled up, as if it were trying to hide beneath your feet at every step. Because the sun's rays shine down from directly overhead, you have almost no shadow at all. Later in the afternoon, when the sun is at a lower angle in the sky, your shadow begins to grow and stretches out like a giant on stilts. Your shadow seems to have a life of its own. It almost seems to laugh as it imitates the things you do, for it exaggerates your movements like a clown.

noon

afternoon

You can't move faster than your shadow. If you jump to one side, it is right there when you land. If you jump straight up, it may leave you for a moment, but it will hurry back and fasten itself to your shoes when you come down again. Have you ever tried to reach out and pick up your shadow? As you reach, it reaches too, so that it is always just beyond your finger tips.

If you walk alone down the sidewalk in the evening, the street light makes your shadow seem even more mysterious. As you walk by the light, your shadow catches up and begins

to pass you, as if it were racing to get away. With every step it grows longer and larger, and finally it stretches farther than you can see into the darkness ahead. Sometimes, if you pass several street lights close together, one shadow becomes two. Then they seem to try to keep from stepping on each other, and suddenly they are gone.

The dark, blank shape of a shadow can represent anything you like. An old tree can become an evil monster, a building can become a castle. Simple outlines turn into fantastic shapes, and familiar objects can cast shadows that look like people, or even animals.

Shadow Animals

Turn on a single light at night in a dark room. Remove the shade or tilt it so that light falls directly on one wall. Stand between the light and the wall, turn sideways to the wall, and place the palms of your hands together, with your thumbs on top, on a level with your eyes. Raise your thumbs and drop the little

finger of your right hand. On the wall the
head of a dog will appear. Move your thumbs,
and the dog will prick up its ears. You can
make the dog bark, pant, or even yawn by
moving your little finger. In the blackness of
the shadow you can imagine the details that
are not there—the nostrils, eyes, and fur. You
will have fun making a lifelike, moving animal with only your two hands.

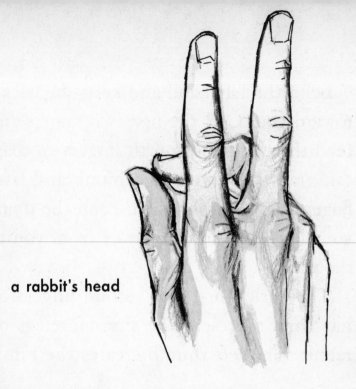

a rabbit's head

With the same two hands you can create a complete rabbit with head, ears, body, hind legs, and tiny forepaws. First hold your right hand upright, with the back toward you, and raise the first two fingers. Touch the last two fingers to your thumb. Move your hand around until its shadow looks like a rabbit's head with two ears sticking up. Now you can build the rest of the rabbit with your left hand.

Bend the left hand and keep the back of it toward you. Curl the first two fingers and extend the third and fourth fingers so that you can grab them with the thumb and last two fingers of your right hand. Point the thumb of your left hand straight away from you under the palm.

The curled first and second fingers of the left hand represent the short forelegs of the rabbit. The left thumb creates the hind legs

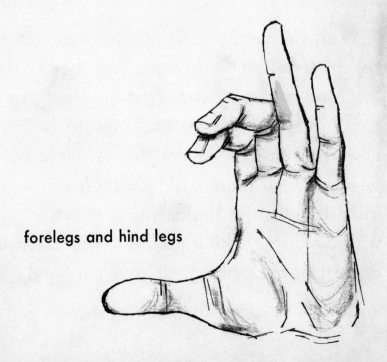

forelegs and hind legs

resting on the ground. Adjust your hands so that the forelegs look very short compared to the long hind legs. After experimenting you will be able to wiggle the little finger of your right hand so that the rabbit seems to be nibbling something. If you are careful, you can straighten the forepaws so that they move up to the rabbit's mouth. It may take some practice to get the rabbit to look right, but the final result will be worth the effort.

The next shadow animal makes use of your arms as well as your two hands. Hold your left hand flat, palm up. Place your right hand palm down on top of it and extend it a little farther forward. Now crook your right thumb up as far as it will go, keeping it sharply bent at the first joint. Watch the shadow you make and move your thumb until its shadow looks like a small hump with a hole in it.

Slowly move your hands apart but keep your arms together at the wrists. The shadow will look something like a lazy crocodile opening its mouth. Now with a little patience you will be able to add some teeth and a tongue. Bend the first finger of each hand at the second joint. When your hands are together, the fingers will not show, but when you open the crocodile's mouth again, he will show a good set of teeth. You will find that a few waggles of

your left thumb will make his tongue move.

In making the crocodile, your arms add to the effect, since they seem to be the long, slim body of the animal. The moves may seem awkward at first, but after you have practiced awhile you will get a vicious-looking crocodile every time. The lifelike look of your animals will depend on your skill.

Shadow Stage

A simple device can be used to make a stage on which your shadow characters can perform. It will also hide your hands from an audience. Hang an old white sheet from a doorway by fastening it at the very top of the wooden door frame with thumbtacks. Do not place the thumbtacks where they will mar the appearance of the wood. Take the shade off a

table lamp and place the lamp on a table about
ten feet behind the doorway. Put another table
in the doorway just behind the sheet, and hang
a heavy blanket from the edge of the table nearest the sheet to the floor. The table top is the
stage for your play, and the shadows cast by
the single lamp will fall on the sheet above
the table.

Your audience sits on the other side of the sheet. Both the room where you are performing and the room in which the observers sit must be as dark as possible. Since your hands cannot be seen, the shadow figures they make will seem almost lifelike. Stand at the side of the door, so that only your arms and hands,

not your body, create shadows. Make your crocodile crawl slowly into view on the table top from the edge of the doorway. After he has yawned a giant yawn and wiggled his tongue, he can retreat. In the same way the other animals you have learned to make can become actors on the shadow stage.

Chinese Shadow Plays

Your shadow theater, made of a sheet, a table, and a doorway, is much like the stage used by the Chinese for shadow plays for over two thousand years. Usually the trees, houses, animals, and people in these plays are all made

23

of wood or cardboard. Dragons and costumed figures have always been popular characters for them.

In a real shadow theater a ground glass screen is often used instead of a sheet, but the general effect is the same. The characters are held close to the screen and are moved by long wires attached to them. In Burma and India, as well as China, shadow plays are often more popular than puppet or marionette shows. The intricate shadow figures can be made to walk and talk, and colored lights can be thrown onto the screen to create the proper mood for each scene.

You can make cardboard shadow characters of your own from the patterns of the dragon and the knight on page 25. Each pattern is drawn on cardboard that has been divided into many small squares. This is done so that

you can cut your figures from sheets of cardboard of any size. Simply divide the cardboard sheet into many smaller squares and fill in each one with the lines shown in the pattern. Draw some characters of your own if you like, but these patterns will help you get started.

Two old coat hangers will make good operating rods for the shadow figures. Straighten

out the hangers and bend each one up at a right angle about two inches from the end with a pair of pliers. Use Scotch tape to fasten the wires to the cardboard.

When you use your shadow figures, move the lamp and its table off to one side. Now you can stand behind the sheet without standing in front of the lamp as you move the figures, and your shadow will not be cast on the sheet. Hold the figures as close to the sheet as possible between the sheet and the lamp, so that the shadows are distinct. If you work the dragon with one hand and the knight with the other, you can create a one-act play.

A good sequence might run as follows. The

knight walks on slowly from one side, looking at the ground. Then the dragon enters from the opposite side. At first the knight does not notice him, but the dragon gives a terrible roar and the knight jumps back. He sees his danger and realizes that he must kill the dragon to keep from being killed himself. The knight lunges at the dragon, only to be knocked flat on his back. There is a struggle as the knight tries to rise. At last after he is almost bitten several times, the knight drives his lance into the monster. The dragon staggers, lets out a terrible cry, and falls on his back, dead at last. The knight, weary but triumphant, slowly pushes the dead dragon off the stage.

The knight
enters.

The dragon
is wounded.

The knight pushes
the dragon away.

Human Shadow Plays

Using a friend as a partner, you can create some live shadows that ought to make everyone laugh. Take the stage table away from the doorway and place the lamp on the floor about ten feet directly behind the sheet. Stand facing your partner halfway between the sheet and the lamp. Take a single step sideways so that you are closer to the sheet than your partner.

29

You are now in a position to do some realistic shadow boxing with your friend. It will seem to the audience that you and your partner are standing opposite each other, and it will look as if your blows are landing directly on each other. A few moans and groans at the right time will add to the illusion.

Probably the most curious effect of all is the way you can make yourself grow or shrink simply by walk-ing closer to the light or closer to the sheet. Try walking straight at the light and then stepping over it. To the audience it will look as if you have grown into a giant several stories tall, and then, when you step over the lamp, as if you have suddenly floated up to the top of the sheet and out of view.

Swing off to one side after you have stepped over the lamp and reappear in your normal size close to the sheet again. You and your partner can create the illusion of a never-ending series of people who come into view from one side of the sheet, quickly grow to giant size in a few strides, and jump through the ceiling! Simply take turns walking in at one side of the sheet, walking toward the light, and stepping over it. Be careful that your

as it looks to
the audience

shadows do not fall on the sheet during the return to the starting point.

There is almost no end to the fun you can have with shadows and shadow plays. The important thing, beside learning to make the shadows properly, is to remember that you are an actor. You must believe in your shadows if the audience is to believe in them too.

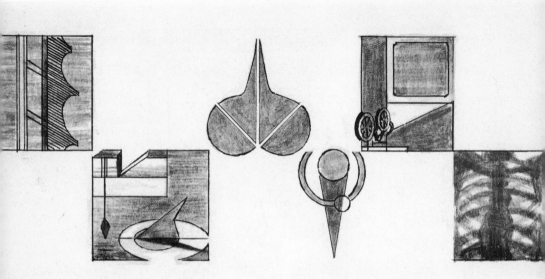

USEFUL SHADOWS

Shadows are more important to us than we sometimes realize. They have helped astronomers discover important facts about our earth, the sun, and the moon. Shadows make it possible to identify objects in aerial photographs that otherwise could not be recognized. For a long time many clocks used shadows for telling time. Slides, movies, and X rays create shadow pictures. All of these examples show how useful shadows can be.

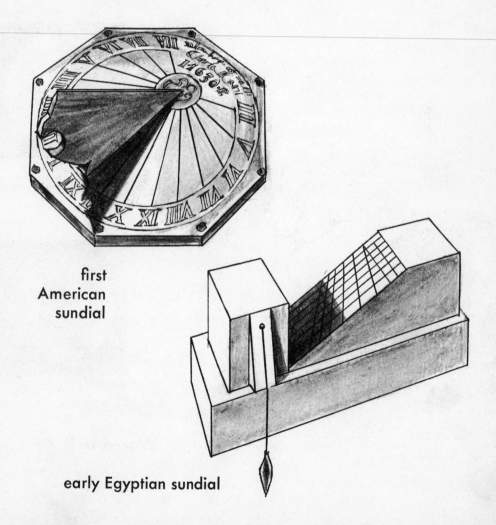

first
American
sundial

early Egyptian sundial

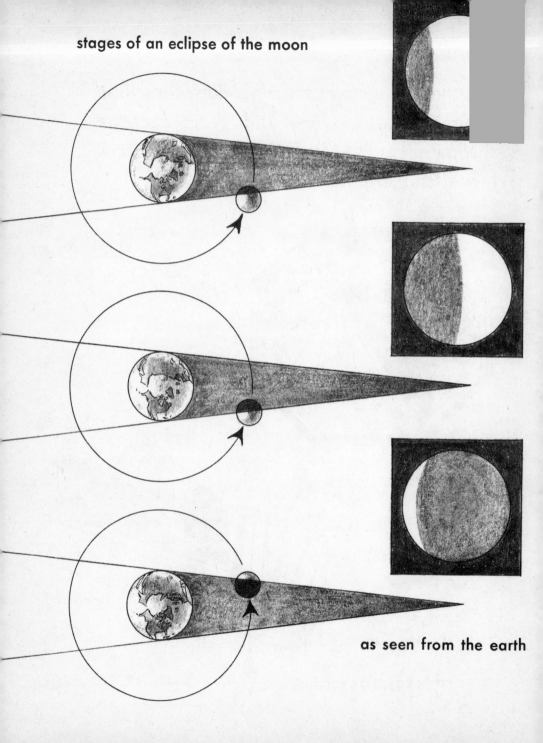

stages of an eclipse of the moon

as seen from the earth

The Earth's Shadow

A single shadow helped men to prove one of the most important facts ever learned about the earth. In the path of the sun's light, the earth casts a cone-shaped shadow out into space for almost a million miles. As the moon circles around the earth, it sometimes passes through this shadow. At such times there is an eclipse of the moon. During an eclipse we can see the shadow of our own planet on the moon if the night sky is clear. Although the area of the shadow is much larger than the moon, we can see the edge of the shadow when the moon enters and leaves it, and it shows a definite curve.

Almost 400 years before the time of Christ, the Greek philosopher Aristotle saw the curved shadow of the earth as it crossed the moon

during an eclipse. He believed that this proved that the earth was round, although most people thought the earth must be flat.

A little more than one hundred years later a Greek mathematician named Eratosthenes used another shadow to prove that the earth was round and to make the first calculation of the total distance around the earth. He knew that in the city Syene there was a deep well. The bottom of this well could be seen only at noon on about June 21 each year. On this day the sun was directly above the well so that its rays shone straight down to the bottom. On the same day in his own city of Alexandria, about 500 miles farther north, shadows were cast at noon, because the sun was not directly overhead. Eratosthenes reasoned that this could happen only if the earth were round.

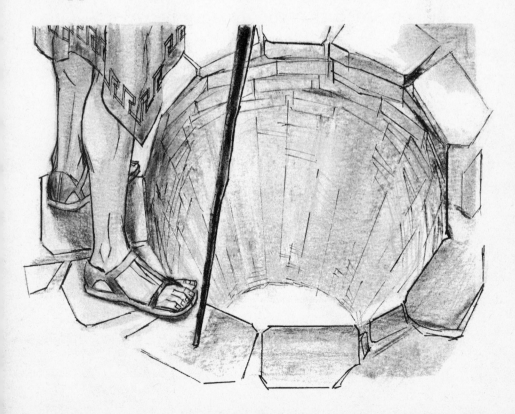

On one June 21 he placed a pole straight up and down in Alexandria and measured the length of the shadow. Knowing the length of the pole, he plotted the triangle formed by the shadow, the pole, and the line of the sun's rays. He figured the angle between the sun's rays and the pole was about 1/50 of a complete circle. Following known geometric principles, he concluded that the distance between Syene,

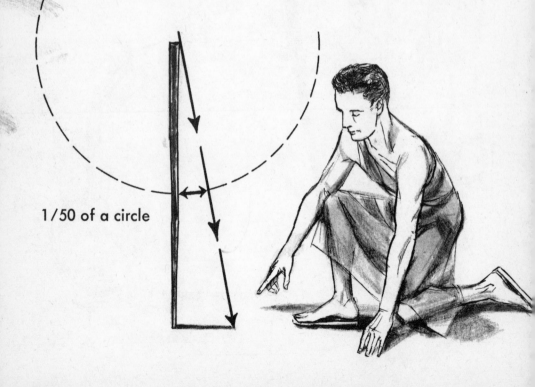

1/50 of a circle

where the sun was overhead, and Alexandria was 1/50 of the distance around the earth. He multiplied the distance between the two cities by 50 and got 25,000 miles as his answer. His result has been found to be only about 100 miles more than today's most accurate measurement. Certainly this was a remarkable achievement, and it was based on the shadow of a stick!

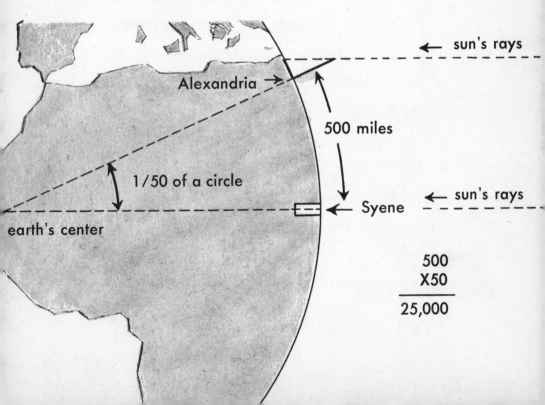

earth's center

1/50 of a circle

Alexandria →

500 miles

← Syene

← sun's rays

← sun's rays

$$\begin{array}{r} 500 \\ \times 50 \\ \hline 25{,}000 \end{array}$$

The Moon's Shadow

Just as the earth casts a shadow in space, so does the moon. When the moon passes between the sun and the earth in just the right position, it creates a round shadow about 167 miles wide that moves slowly across the earth as the moon circles and the earth turns. People located in the path of the shadow see what is called a total eclipse of the sun. For a few minutes the moon completely blocks out the giant disc of the sun. Astronomers can predict when an eclipse will occur, and at such times they often travel to the areas of the earth that will fall in the path of the moon's shadow.

From the darkness of the shadow a halo of the sun's glowing gases can be seen projecting

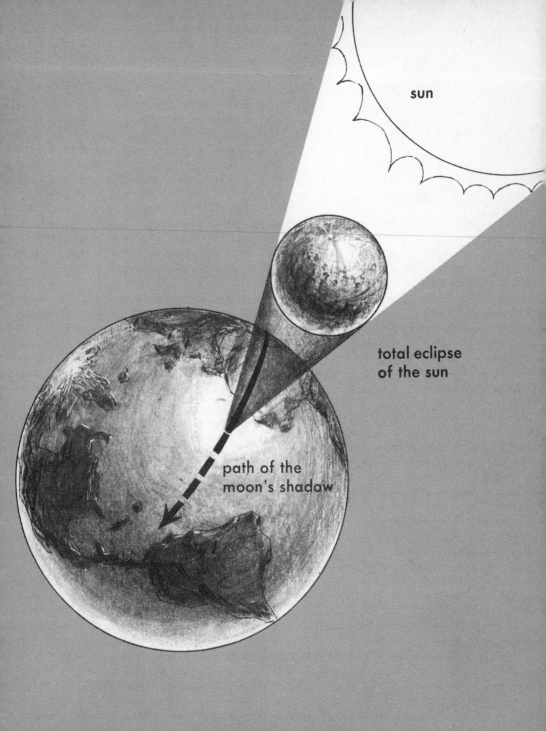

sun

total eclipse
of the sun

path of the
moon's shadow

total eclipse of the sun

beyond the black circle of the moon. These gases, at times reaching out as far as 100,000 miles, can best be seen during a total eclipse of the sun. For a few short minutes the precious shadow makes possible observations and photographs of the sun that otherwise could not be made.

Shadows on the Moon

Astronomers use shadows to measure the height of the mountains and the depth of the craters on the moon. As the moon changes from a narrow crescent to a full disc each month, the angle at which the sun's rays strike

crescent

full moon

crescent

first quarter

last quarter

The terminator crosses the visible surface of the moon twice every 29 ½ days.

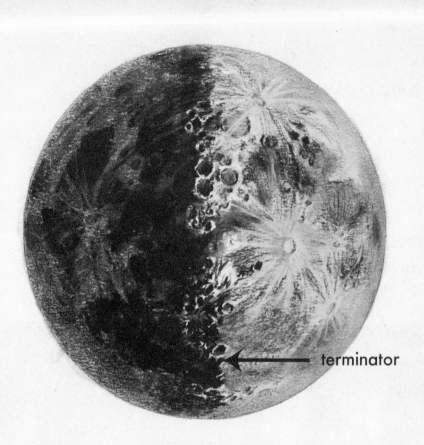

terminator

each part of the moon's visible surface con-
stantly changes. The line that divides the light
area from the dark is called the terminator.
Each month the terminator slowly crosses and
recrosses the moon. Near the terminator the

46

features of the moon cast long, sharp shadows. When a mountain on the moon casts a long shadow, it is easy to tell the shape of the top of the mountain from the edge of the shadow. The lengths of the shadows along the terminator can be compared to give the height of the mountains and depth of the craters.

With an ordinary pair of binoculars, you may be able to see the shadows of some of the features of the moon. Without these shadows it would be impossible to learn much about our nearest neighbor in space.

Shadows in Aerial Photographs

Try this experiment with a pin, a sheet of white cardboard, and a single light bulb and cord. First darken the room so that your light bulb is the only source of light. Next stick the pin into the cardboard so that it is straight up and down.

Hold the light directly above the pin. Now if you look down on the pin, you will see only the round head of the pin and practically no shadow. Move the light to one side so that the rays strike the pin at an angle. Now, even though you are still looking straight down on the pin, you can see a sharp shadow, which shows the pin as it would look from the side.

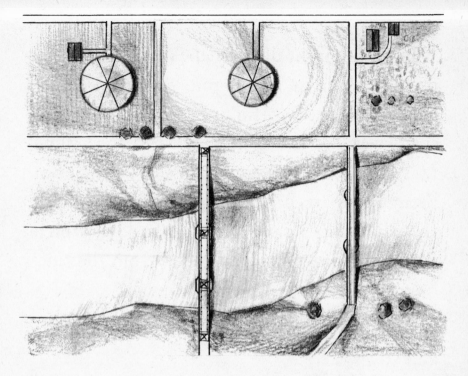

This principle is important in making aerial photographs. When you look down on trees and houses from above, it is hard to see them clearly. In a photograph taken at noon, a tall water tower may look the same as a low, circular container for storing farm products. A large suspension bridge may look about the same as a smaller bridge.

In a photograph taken at five o'clock, however, the shadow of the water tower will outline the long, slender legs and crossbars of the tower and the tank at the top. The circular grain bin will cast a much smaller shadow, which will have a narrow half-moon shape. The two similar bridges can now be distinguished

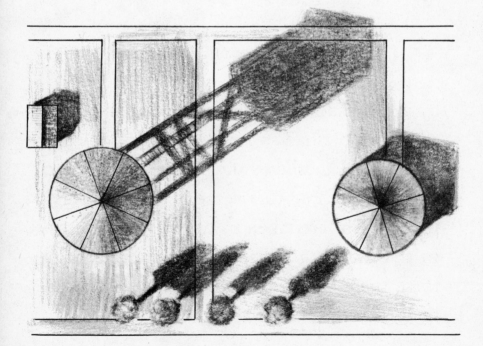

by their shadows. The smaller one casts a narrow strip of shadow; the shadow of the suspension bridge shows the outlines of its cables and towers. For this reason, the best aerial photographs are taken in bright sunlight early in the morning or late in the afternoon. At these times the shadows have a chance to tell their story.

Sundial Shadows

If you had been born more than two hundred years ago, you probably would have told time with a sundial rather than with a mechanical clock or wrist watch. A sundial is made of a slanting stick which casts a shadow on a dial on which marks are placed to represent the

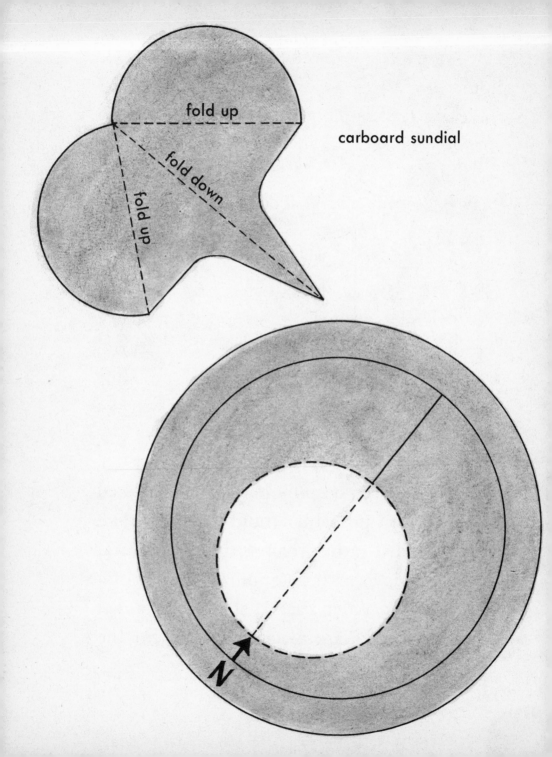

fold up

carboard sundial

fold down

fold up

N

hours of the day from sunrise to sunset. As the earth rotates, the sun's position seems to change, just as the hour hand of a clock moves around.

For a completely accurate sundial, the slanting stick must point toward the north star and the hour marks must be figured mathematically. But a dial that will work well can be made from the pattern on page 54. Trace each shape onto cardboard with carbon paper, and cut them out as carefully as you can. Glue the triangular marker to the round dial on the dotted lines.

Take the dial outside and set it on a level spot so that the marker points north. You can use a pocket compass to check directions. Dur-

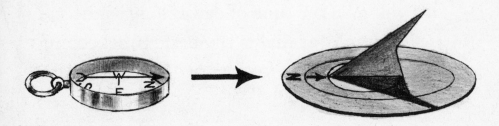

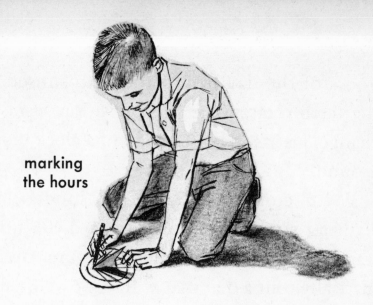

marking
the hours

ing the day keep an eye on the clock and mark
each full hour on the dial by making a dot at
the edge of each hourly position of the shadow.
Be careful not to move the dial during the day.
When you have made a dot for each hour between sunrise and sunset, draw lines with a
ruler connecting each dot to the base of the
marker. Number each hour and then your sundial will give the time of day as long as the sun
is shining. Your dial is the basic timekeeping
device used by men for over two thousand years.

Projected Shadows

Did it ever occur to you that slides and movies are very much like your homemade shadow plays? The important difference is that a lens has been added so that small pictures can be focused on a large screen. What we see on the projection screen are the shadows cast by the darker areas of the slides or films. Areas that are not completely dark will cast only partial shadows, so that instead of seeing only a sharp silhouette of black against white, we

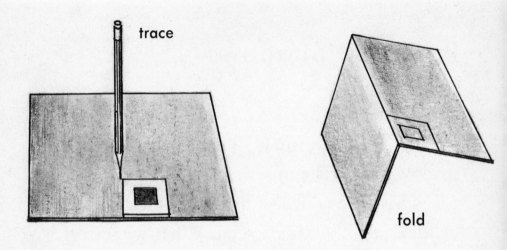

trace

fold

can see many shades of dark and light. If you or your friends have a slide projector, you can make and project your own shadow slides.

On a thin piece of cardboard trace around the shape of one of the regular picture slides that fit your projector. Fold the cardboard along one edge of the outline. Cut through both thicknesses around the remaining part of the outline, and you will have two rec-tangles of cardboard hinged together. Now

cut

glue

cut the inside out of each flap so that you have a small double picture frame. Get a small piece of transparent cellophane paper from a food wrapper and cut it to fit inside the cardboard frame you have made. Glue the cardboard and cellophane together with household cement and place the frame under a book to dry.

Use India ink to draw pictures on the cellophane paper. You can buy a small bottle of this ink at a stationery or art supply store. You can draw landscapes, people, animals, or even make up a sequence. If you take the time to make four or five more blank cellophane slides like the first one, you will have enough to tell a story with your shadow drawings.

A shadow very much like those made by slides and movies is the shadow in an X-ray photograph. In this case the energy wave lengths are so short they are invisible, but they can create an image on a photographic plate like ordinary light. Although X rays can

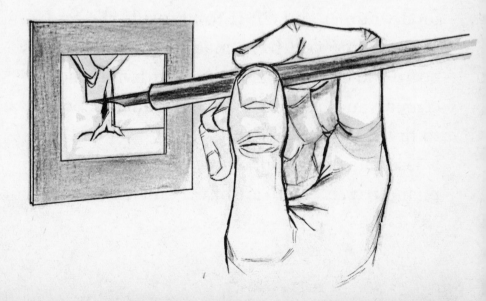

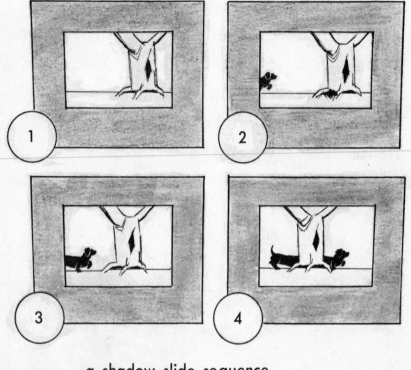

a shadow slide sequence

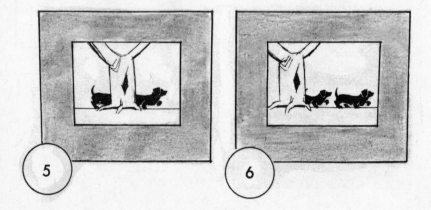

pass through solid objects, they are able to penetrate some materials better than others. Objects that tend to block the X rays to a greater extent cast darker shadows.

When an X-ray picture is taken of your chest, the invisible rays tend to be blocked more by bone than by skin and muscle tissue. The

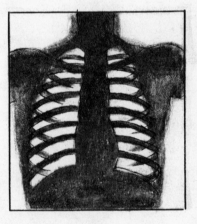

normal chest X ray
positive print

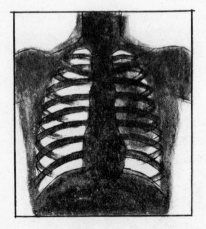

shadow caused
by tuberculosis

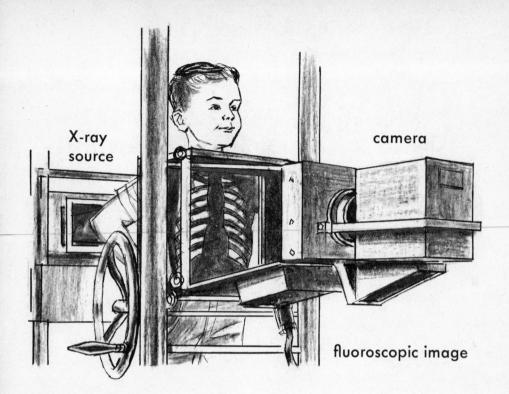

fluoroscopic image

unseen shadows are captured on a photographic plate and in this way become visible.

X-ray pictures can be seen in motion on a screen in a machine called a fluoroscope. Often both fluoroscopic images and chest X-ray photographs are used to detect shadows revealing diseases such as tuberculosis. Thus X-ray shadows can help to guard your health.

Whether you are looking at your X-ray shadow or your ordinary shadow, that shadow is a part of you. In the same way many other shadows are a part of your life. Men have long been fascinated by them, and they have made many important discoveries because of them.

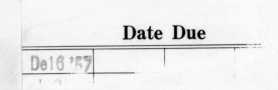

Franz Brandenberg

A FUN WEEKEND

pictures by
Alexa Brandenberg

Greenwillow Books  New York

For Alexa
—F. B.

For Mark
—A. B.

Colored pencils, watercolors, and a black pen were
used for the full-color art. The text type is ITC Bookman.

Library of Congress Cataloging-in-Publication Data
Brandenberg, Franz.
A fun weekend / by Franz Brandenberg;
pictures by Alexa Brandenberg.
p. cm.
Summary: Although their trip to the country does
not go as planned, a family has a great deal of fun.
ISBN 0-688-09720-0. ISBN 0-688-09721-9 (lib. bdg.)
[1. Vacations—Fiction.] I. Brandenberg, Alexa, ill.
II. Title. PZ7.B7364Fu 1991
[E]—dc20 89-77502 CIP AC

"We'll go to the country and stay

overnight," said Mother.

"What fun!" said Adrian and Paula.

"The two of you will have your own
room," said Father.

"I don't like to sleep in a separate
room," said Adrian.

"Neither do I," said Paula.

"You do at home," said Mother.

"That's different," said Adrian.

"In a strange place, I like to be
with you."

"Don't worry," said Father. "We'll
be right next door."

"I'll bring iced tea and sandwiches,"
said Mother.
"Couldn't we eat in a restaurant?"
asked Adrian and Paula.
"We'll see," said Mother.

"Let's go!" said Father. "It's a long drive."

"Half the fun is getting there," said Mother.
They piled into the car and drove through
the countryside.

"Could we stop in the woods, please?"
asked Adrian.

"It might be good for us to unwind a bit,"
said Mother.

"But just a bit," said Father. "Or we'll never
make it to the lodge in time."

They stopped in the woods and
stretched their legs.
"That was fun!" they said, as they
piled back into the car and
drove off.

"Could we stop for a swim, please?"
asked Paula.

"We'll never make it to the lodge in
time," said Father.

"Just a quick dip to cool off," said
Mother.

"All right," said Father. "But, please,
let's make it quick."

They stopped at the lake and had
a quick dip.

"That was great," they said, as
they piled back into the car and
drove off.

"Could we stop for ice cream,
  please?" asked Adrian.
"We'll never make it to the lodge
  in time," said Father.
"I feel like having some myself,"
  said Mother.
"All right," said Father. "I'll have
  some, too."

They stopped at the ice cream parlor
and had ice cream cones.
"Delicious," they said, as they piled
back into the car and drove off.

"Could we make a brief stop at that
crafts shop, please?" asked Mother.
"Why not?" said Father. "We stopped
for everyone else. But, please, let's make
it brief."
"Stops at shops are never brief,"
said Adrian.

They stopped at the crafts shop and
shopped and shopped.

"That was fun!" they said, as they piled
back into the car and drove off.

"I have to stop for gas," said Father.

"We'll never make it to the lodge in time,"
said Paula.

"I'll just be a minute," said Father.

They stopped at the gas station and
waited in the car.

When the tank was full, and Father had
paid, they drove on.

"I have to go to the bathroom," said Paula.

"Why didn't you go at the gas station?"
asked Mother.

"If you have to go, you have to go," said
Father. "But please hurry up."
They stopped at a public toilet, and they
all took their turns.

"That was a good idea, Paula," they said, as
they piled back into the car and drove off.

By the time they made it to the lodge,
it was night.

Father went inside. When he came
back, he said, "We arrived too late.

"They didn't keep our rooms."

"Too bad," said Mother.

"At least we had fun getting here,"

said Adrian.

"Where are we going to sleep?"
asked Paula.
"Right here in the car," said
Father. "The lodge loaned us
some blankets."

"And how are we going to eat?"

asked Adrian.

"The dining room is closed,"

said Father.

"We still have the sandwiches

and iced tea," said Mother.

"It will be a picnic," said Paula.

"And we won't have to brush
our teeth!" said Adrian.

"Yes, we will!" said Father.

"Where?" asked Paula.

"The manager said we could
use one of the bathrooms," said Father.

They had a nice picnic.

Then they took their washcloths

and toothbrushes and went to

the bathroom.

"Now we are ready for bed,"

they said, as they piled back into the car.

They cuddled up in the seats and
wrapped themselves in the blankets.
"This is more fun than a room in the
lodge," said Adrian.
"But not as comfortable," said Paula.
"It's only for a night," said Mother.
"Tomorrow we'll be back home in
our own beds."
"If we get back in time," said Father.
"It's a long drive, with all our stops."

"Half the fun is getting there,"
said Paula.
"And the other half is being all
together," said Adrian.